An Hachette UK Company
www.hachette.co.uk

Summersdale Publishers Ltd
Part of Octopus Publishing Group Limited
Carmelite House
50 Victoria Embankment
LONDON
EC4Y 0DZ
UK

www.summersdale.com

Printed and bound in China

ISBN: 978-1-78685-266-3

Substantial discounts on bulk quantities of Summersdale books are available to corporations, professional associations and other organisations. For details contact general enquiries: telephone: +44 (0) 1243 771107 or email: enquiries@summersdale.com.

Disclaimer: No animals were harmed in the creation of this book.

To........................
From.....................

Oh hello.

Fuzzberta and her furriends are going on some grand adventures.

Won't you come along?

Doughnut worry, be happy.

(MiniGuineaPig says hi)

My log has a message fur you...

(Jennifuzz's log says hi)

Rub a dub dub,
three cubs in a tub.

(Shnoopy, Billy Blob and Jelly Baby salute you)

This Batman is too smol.

Wonder Woman is
quite robust though.

Cartman also seems
more robust than usual.

Let's get fuzzical!

(Fuzzberta always skips leg day)

Treat yo' self.

Just keep swimming.

(You can keep nomming too)

Fur sure, dude.

All the round things are having a party!

Aren't you a little young to be drinking, Fuzzberta?

Fuzz and Loathing
in Blob Vegas

The Good, the Bad and the Fuzzy

Q: Which course does
Professor Berta teach?

A: Intro to Fuzz-ics!

Actual photo of
**George Washington
founding America.**

Fuzzlock Holmes
has a Case of the Doughnut Lips.

Blob Save the Queen!

My hands are
YUUUUUGE!

From Fuzzia with Love

The Pawmaid's Tale

(Blessed be the fuzz)

Is it just me, or does the Sphinx look extra round today?

'Her life amongst the intellectuals of post-war Paris would later inspire her memoir, *A Moveable Fuzz*.'

The Rather Small Gatsby
by F. Scott Fuzzgerald

The Royal Tenenblobs

Boldly going where no fuzz
has gone before.

Q: What's a pirate's favourite food?

A: C-AARRRRR-ots!

Little Red Riding Fuzz, those treats were for Grandma!

SHAME!! SHAME!!!

You know fuzzing,
Jon Snow.

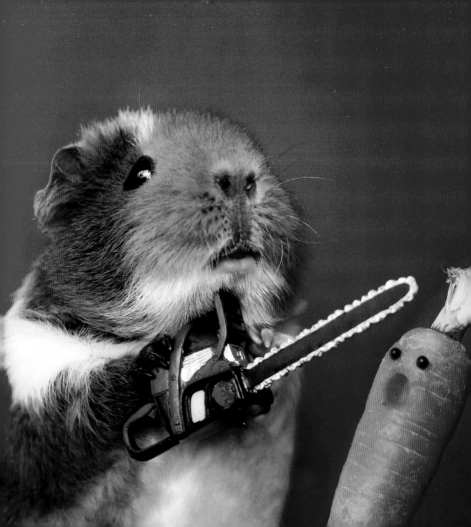

SO HANGRY!

Fuzz of the North

brings you provisions.

You ever get the
feeling your ice cream is
smiling at you?

How does Blorpy Claus even
fit down that chimney?

We'll never know.

Q: What's Fuzzberta's favourite pancake topping?

A: More pancakes!

O Fuzzer,
where art thou?

What is Fuzzberta
listening to?

Piggy Stardust,

of course.

Fun Fact:

Fuzzberta played the guitar solo
of 'Bohemian Rhapsody'.

Shnoop Dogg
chubbyizzle fuzzizzle

Neener! Neener!
Your meatball is mocking you!

Practice makes perfect!

(Even for guinea pigs, apparently)

Always be yourself.

(Unless you can be a dinosaur)

That's all, folks.
See you again soon!

Fuzzberta & Friends

is about sharing happiness,
one doughnut lip at a time. Follow
our blobby adventures online!

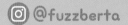 @fuzzberta  facebook.com/fuzzberta

PS Please visit our rescue furriends at **thepipsqueakery.org**!

If you're interested in finding out more about our books, find us on Facebook at Summersdale Publishers and follow us on Twitter at @Summersdale.

www.summersdale.com